A NEW DIRECTION

A Cognitive-Behavioral Treatment Curriculum

WORKBOOK

Co-occurring Disorders

Mapping a Life
of Recovery & Freedom
for Chemically Dependent
Criminal Offenders

**A Collaboration of Chemical Dependency Professionals from
the Minnesota Department of Corrections and the Hazelden Foundation**

HAZELDEN®

Hazelden
Center City, Minnesota 55012-0176

1-800-328-9000
1-651-213-4590 (Fax)
www.hazelden.org

ISBN: 1-59285-138-X

Cover design by David Spohn
Interior design by Terri Kinne
Illustrations by Patrice Barton

Editor's Note
This material was written to educate individuals about chemical dependency and mental illness. It is not intended as a substitute for professional medical or psychiatric care.

Any stories or case studies that may be used in this material are composites of many individuals. Names and details have been changed to protect identities.

Hazelden, a national nonprofit organization founded in 1949, helps people reclaim their lives from the disease of addiction. Built on decades of knowledge and experience, Hazelden offers a comprehensive approach to addiction that addresses the full range of patient, family, and professional needs, including treatment and continuing care for youth and adults, research, higher learning, public education and advocacy, and publishing.

A life of recovery is lived "one day at a time." Hazelden publications, both educational and inspirational, support and strengthen lifelong recovery. In 1954, Hazelden published *Twenty-Four Hours a Day*, the first daily meditation book for recovering alcoholics, and Hazelden continues to publish works to inspire and guide individuals in treatment and recovery, and their loved ones. Professionals who work to prevent and treat addiction also turn to Hazelden for evidence-based curricula, informational materials, and videos for use in schools, treatment programs, and correctional programs.

Through published works, Hazelden extends the reach of hope, encouragement, help, and support to individuals, families, and communities affected by addiction and related issues.

For questions about Hazelden publications,
please call **800-328-9000** or visit us online at **hazelden.org/bookstore**.

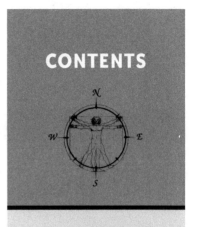

CONTENTS

A NEW DIRECTION

A Cognitive-Behavioral Treatment Curriculum

Acknowledgments

*The following people, whose titles and positions are listed
as held upon publication, have contributed to this curriculum:*

Joan Fabian
Commissioner, Minnesota Department of Corrections

Nick Motu
Executive Vice President, Hazelden Publishing and Educational Services

James D. Kaul, Ph.D.
Director, TRIAD Chemical Dependency Program
Minnesota Department of Corrections

Minnesota Department of Corrections

Sex Offender Treatment Program at Lino Lakes Minnesota Correctional Facility
Jim Berg, Program Supervisor
Kevin Nelson, Corrections Program Therapist

TRIAD Chemical Dependency Program at Lino Lakes Minnesota Correctional Facility
Randy Tenge, Corrections Supervisor
Jackie Michaelson, Corrections Program Therapist
Linda Rose, Corrections Program Therapist

Shakopee Minnesota Correctional Facility
Judy Squires, Corrections Program Therapist

Central Office
Jeff Brown, Ph.D., L.P., Associate Director of Behavioral Health Services

In Addition:

Writer: Joseph M. Moriarity. **Designer:** Terri Kinne.
Typesetters: Terri Kinne and Julie Szamocki. **Illustrator:** Patrice Barton.
Prepress: Don Freeman, Kathryn Kjorlien, Joan Erickson, David Spohn.
Editor: Corrine Casanova. **Copy editor:** Catherine Broberg. **Proofreader:** Judith Peacock.

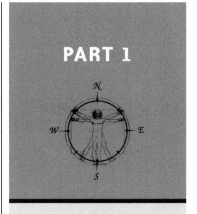

What You Are Dealing With

Your addiction to alcohol and/or other drugs has gotten you where you are now. Maybe you've been told that you are depressed or traumatized too. These mental health issues need to be looked at while you are in this treatment program. You are not alone. Read the following stories to learn more.

Terrell's Story

I'm twenty-two years old doing time in a maximum-security prison. I'm in a drug treatment program, but they also have me on a drug because I have what is called "bipolar disorder" and I need the medication to stay level.

When I was out on the street, I was into just about every-thing—dealing drugs, petty theft, and so on. I got away with it at first, and then I started to believe that I was a criminal mastermind. You know, a real Al Capone. I was drinking and doing a little coke here and there, driving a tricked-out ride, and wearing all the bling-bling. I thought I was on top of the world.

Then slowly, I began to notice a change. I was feeling "high" even without the cocaine, and that scared me. So I drank more to help me feel normal. Then I felt real low for days at a time. I even would think about killing myself—but I found out that cocaine would help snap me out of that.

Eventually, I was using more drugs than I was selling and I had trouble affording all the things I was buying. To me, it didn't matter because I thought I could do anything. I stayed up all night hatching criminal plans that I thought were foolproof even though they were nothing more than scribbled notes written on scraps of paper.

My personal life was a mess. One day, I just couldn't keep it together and decided to knock off a liquor store—and that's how I got here.

— Terrell, age 22

Carmen's Story

I'm thirty years old. They tell me that I've been messed up since I was a teen. See, in high school, I fell in with the wrong crowd. We would skip school all the time and smoke pot. One day, a friend of mine brought a couple of hits of acid with him and, man, was I hooked. I went places that I never thought existed, all in my own mind.

Eventually, I was taking it on a regular basis, until the day I had a really bad trip. I don't remember much about it, but they say that I overdosed and almost died. For some odd reason, I was never placed in a treatment program. I guess my parents thought that the OD scared me straight. It scared me, all right, but only enough that I quit taking acid. I kept on smoking pot.

In my early twenties, I started hearing voices telling me to hurt my parents. I kept saying no to them, but the voices kept on screaming at me to attack them. My parents knew something was up because I was acting so strangely, so they took me to the hospital again. I didn't like the way I felt on the medication they gave me there, but maybe that had something to do with the pot I was smoking again. I decided to go off of my meds, and then the voices came back. They sounded so real, and I thought that if I did what they told me to do, they would go away for good. I did, but they didn't! That was a long time ago, but the voices are still with me. They are not too bad as long as I take my medication and don't smoke weed.

I've been sober now for two years, and they say that if I stay sober and keep managing my symptoms, I will probably be released.

— Carmen, age 30

David's Story

I once thought that I had a great life. A perfect family, two kids, a dog, a boat in the garage. You know, the picket fence kind of thing. For some reason, that just wasn't enough. I started to feel down all the time like nothing was good enough. I had thought that keeping up with others like me would make me happy, but it didn't.

At first, when I went out after work to have a drink, I would feel better, like all that other stuff didn't matter. After a while, a few drinks didn't cut it, so I started drinking more and spending all my time at the bar. That's when my old lady started laying into me when I got home each night. She was telling me not to spend so much time at the bar, but I didn't listen.

I finally couldn't take it anymore and I hit her. I know now that it wasn't her fault, but I thought it was at the time. She said she wasn't going to put up with it, so she went out and got a legal separation and I moved into an efficiency apartment across town.

I knew that I couldn't have that. It would ruin my so-called perfect life. That's when I started stalking her, watching where she was going day and night. I eventually lost my job, so I was able to use even more time to intimidate her. That's when a restraining order was slapped on me. I was so angry.

One night, I got really drunk, called her on the phone, and some strange man answered. I was so angry that I got in my car and drove over there. As I pulled into the driveway, a couple of cop cars pulled up too. I got nabbed for violating the restraining order and got a DUI.

I'm only serving a short time, but so far I've learned that I suffer from both alcoholism and depression. As long as I keep seeing my therapist, go to AA (Alcoholics Anonymous) meetings regularly, and learn to control my anger, I think I am going to be okay.

— David, age 27

Like Terrell, Carmen, and David in the examples on the previous pages, you have two illnesses: addiction to alcohol and/or other drugs *and* mental health issues like bipolar disorder, schizophrenia, or depression. It's what we call *co-occurring disorders.* That's the bad news. The really good news is that you *can* learn to manage both. But you can't do this alone. You'll need lots of help from a counselor, a support group, a doctor who knows about mental health, and your group. It will take some hard work from you too, but you *can* get better.

Help Is on the Way

This workbook is designed for people like you who have co-occurring disorders. It will help you make a recovery plan and take care of your mental health issues. By working through it, you'll learn more about

- how to accept the mental health issues you're dealing with

- how your brain works

- how your mental health issues affect the way you think and the decisions you make

- how alcohol and other drugs affect your brain, your body, and your mental health issues

- how your own problems/diagnosis/history have affected the way you think and behave

Co-occurring Disorders

A person who has *co-occurring disorders* is addicted to alcohol and/or other drugs *and* has mental health issues such as major depression, schizophrenia, or a personality disorder.

- how your own criminal thinking patterns have affected the way you think and behave

- how medications can help lessen or take away the symptoms of your mental health issues

- how certain actions, places, and feelings can trigger a relapse for you—and what you can do to handle them to avoid relapse

- how to live a positive, happier life free of addiction and with your mental health issues under control

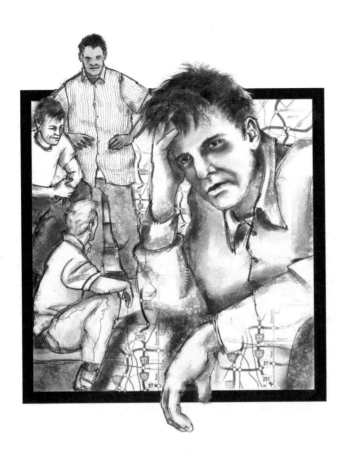

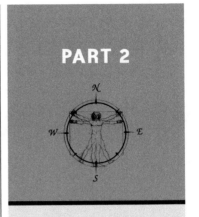
Why Treatment?

In early recovery, you need to be focusing on getting your symptoms stable and working on your recovery plan. But to do that, you first have to be able to see the symptoms and problems that led you to treatment for your co-occurring disorders.

A symptom is something people experience in how they look, feel, think, or act that's different from what's normal—and that generally means they have an illness. Let's start this section by looking at some of your symptoms. Then we'll see how they affect your life.

EXERCISE 1 EXERCISE

Why Are You Here?

➤ Here is a list of items that lead people to enter a treatment program. Put a check next to any items that played a role in your coming to treatment (no matter if you came on your own or because of a court order).

____ depression

____ very high moods (manic behavior)

____ hurting yourself (cutting or burning yourself, overdosing on pills, and so on)

____ violence toward others

____ suicidal thoughts

____ severe agitation

____ anxiety

____ illness caused because you quit taking medications

____ bad temper problems

____ frequent suspicious feelings toward others

____ unusual thoughts

____ hallucinations

____ not taking care of yourself

____ feeling disoriented

___ frequent hostile feelings toward others

___ not having much feeling about anything

___ tension

___ being easily distracted

___ feeling hyper a lot

___ trouble sleeping at night

___ severe panic attacks

___ obsessive thoughts (thinking about certain things over and over again)

___ compulsive rituals (counting, checking, and so on)

___ trouble with the law

___ no place to live

___ lack of money

___ pushed by family to get treatment

___ pushed by the legal system or social services to get treatment

___ sexual problems

___ hearing voices

___ having paranoid, unusual, or very strange thoughts

___ alcohol abuse or addiction

___ crack/cocaine abuse or addiction

___ use of methamphetamine

___ other drug abuse or addiction (heroin, pot, pills, hallucinogens, and so on)

___ compulsive gambling

____ compulsive sexual behavior

____ serious problems with roommates, friends, spouse, partner, or other family members

____ unable to take care of yourself

➤ List any other mental health issues or personal problems that played a part in your need to be in treatment.

_____

_____

_____

_____

_____

_____

_____

_____

A symptom is something people experience in how they look, feel, think, or act that's different from what's normal.

Mental Health, Addiction, and Criminal Activity

Mental health issues, addiction, and criminal activity can affect any area of your life. This includes your health; your relationships with family, friends, and co-workers; where you live; how you live your life; and how you find happiness. This is a great time to look at how your addiction and mental health affect your life. These issues may be hard to face at first, but doing so will be worth it.

➤ For each item in the left-hand column on page 12, put a check in the box under mental health issues, alcohol/drug use, and/or criminal activity if those issues have affected you.

EXAMPLE:

	Mental health issues	Alcohol/drug use	Criminal activity
Physical health, including medical and dental problems	✔	✔	
Work or school	✔	✔	✔

In this example above, the person has checked two boxes next to physical health. Mental health issues have affected his health because he knew something was wrong but wouldn't go to the doctor because he didn't feel comfortable going there. His meth use caused his teeth to rot, but he never went to the dentist until it was too late.

	Mental health issues	Alcohol/drug use	Criminal activity
Physical health, including medical and dental problems			
Diet and eating habits			
Sexual desire or behavior			
Exercise habits			
Self-esteem or confidence			
Relationships with parents			
Relationship with spouse or partner			
Relationships with children			
Relationships with boss and co-workers			
Relationships with friends			
Spirituality (relationship with God, Higher Power, religious practice, and so on)			
Work or school			
Lost opportunities			
Hobbies or recreational activities			
Finances			
Legal problems			

➤ Look at your answers on the previous page. In just a few sentences, describe how your mental health, alcohol/drug use, and criminal activity have affected your life.

_____

_____

_____

_____

_____

EXERCISE 3 EXERCISE

Looking at a Recent Problem

➤ Think of an actual problem you had in the last two or three days. Describe the problem here.

_____

_____

_____

_____

➤ Fill out a Thinking Report (shown on the next page) for the problem you described above.

Thinking Report

1. **Event** _____

   _____

   _____

   _____

   _____

2. **Thoughts** _____

   _____

   _____

   _____

   _____

3. **Feelings** _____

   _____

   _____

   _____

   _____

4. **Behavior** _____

   _____

   _____

   _____

   _____

Answer the following questions:

➤ How did your mental health symptoms affect your thoughts about this problem?

_____

_____

_____

_____

➤ How did your mental health symptoms affect your behavior?

_____

_____

_____

_____

➤ What could you do differently to handle this situation in a more positive way?

_____

_____

_____

_____

Understanding Mental Health Issues

A mental health issue (mental disorder) is a condition that includes a group of symptoms that can affect you for life. Symptoms may be physical, mental, psychological (connected to emotions or coping), or social. You can be affected just a little, a medium amount, or a lot. Mental health issues can even be deadly.

A mental disorder can be a "single episode" where the symptoms last for a period of time and then go away and never return. For example, many people with major depression have it only once in their lives.

Some disorders are "recurrent." That means they happen two or more different times in a person's life. Months or years can pass between episodes, and the person may feel and act okay in between them.

Mental disorders can also be "chronic," meaning that some symptoms and disability are always there, even if the person receives treatment. Carmen, for example, is taking medication for schizophrenia. However, she still hears voices in her head every day. The good news is that they do not bother her as much as they did in the past. She knows now that the voices aren't real and that she can ignore them.

What Causes Co-occurring Disorders?

There is no one cause or reason why a person develops co-occurring disorders. Here are four possible causes:

Genetics. This means that many mental health issues run in families. If others in your family (like a sister, brother, parent, or grandparent) are chemically dependent or have other mental health issues, you are more likely to have the same issues.

There is no one cause or reason why a person develops co-occurring disorders.

Biology. Certain drugs can temporarily or permanently affect the way your brain works. Some drugs (inhalants, methamphetamine, alcohol, Valium) actually change the way your brain works.

Psychology. This affects how you think about things and your reaction to different things. It includes how you feel about yourself and the world you live in. Your personality and how you deal with problems affect your mental health.

Social contacts. This is all about your relationships with family, friends, and other people around you. For example, growing up in a violent family can bring on symptoms of anxiety or depression.

The Relationship between Addiction and Mental Heath Issues

Having mental health issues increases your risk of having an addiction. There are many reasons people with mental health issues use drugs:

- To cover up uncomfortable feelings.

- To help them feel more "normal."

- Because they don't like the way their medications make them feel. Carmen experienced this. She said:

    I didn't like the way I felt on the medication . . . but maybe that had something to do with the pot I was smoking again. I decided to go off of my meds, and then the voices came back.

- For the same reason everyone else does—because they like it and they like to get high.

Follow your treatment plan or take your prescription medications. Not doing so can cause you to return to using drugs.

Addiction to alcohol and other drugs is powerful. It increases your chance of having mental health problems. Alcohol and other drugs prevent prescription medications from working like they should.

Addiction and mental health issues can develop at different times. Sometimes, the mental health issues come before the addiction. Other times, the addiction comes before the mental health issues.

Consider Trisha's story:

> *Trisha, who's twenty-six, had always been kind of anxious, especially at parties or at other group things. She felt like people were saying bad things about her. She began using marijuana to help her relax around others. Soon, she was smoking every day. One afternoon while high, she began to hear voices, but there was no one around. She became very afraid. She thought her neighbors were watching her and planning to kill her so they could steal her car. She ran outside and began threatening her neighbors, so they called the police. She got medical help and found she needed medications.*

Effects of Co-occurring Disorders

Mental health issues or addiction can affect almost every part of your life. This includes your body, how you feel about yourself, how you get along with other people, and some of the goals you set for yourself. Having both an addiction *and* mental health issues (co-occurring disorders) affects your life even more.

Acceptance

Not accepting your mental health issues or addiction—or both—can really get in the way of your getting well. To recover, you need to accept that you have co-occurring disorders and need help. This help may come from a counselor, a self-help group, and/or prescription medications.

Denial of addiction can show up by

- telling yourself that your addiction and its effects aren't really a problem
- blaming your alcohol or other drug use on your mental health issues
- failing to accept that you have to quit alcohol and other drugs
- quitting one drug but continuing to use others
- telling yourself that the effects of addiction on your mental health issues really aren't all that big

Denial of mental health issues can show up by

- having a hard time accepting them
- blaming your behavior on the effects of substances or other factors
- telling yourself that your abnormal behavior is fine and justifying it
- not looking for the help you need and continuing to hurt the people you care about most

Maybe other people in your life are in denial about your situation too. Maybe they have told you that you need to be tougher, not be so lazy, or should really just want to get better. Maybe they said you don't need professional help or medications, that just trying harder would make you better. Those ideas are another kind of denial too.

The easiest way to break your denial is to really look at the symptoms of your co-occurring disorders. Then, look at the effect they have had on your life. The following exercises will help you do this.

EXERCISE **4** EXERCISE

Denying Your Co-occurring Disorders

➤ List two ways you have denied your mental health issues.

EXAMPLE: *"I told myself that the reason I got involved in so many things—things I never finished—was that I was just a high-energy person."*

1. _____

_____

2. _____

_____

➤ List two ways you have denied your addiction.

EXAMPLES: *"Because I didn't use drugs every day, I was sure I wasn't addicted."*

"I told myself that I wasn't that bad off because I knew others who used a whole lot more drugs than I did."

1. _____

_____

2. _____

_____

Preventing Denial in the Future

➤ List two ways you can help stop your denial in the future.

EXAMPLES: *"I have a better chance of seeing the truth about my addiction if I stay involved in Narcotics Anonymous meetings."*

"Talking with my therapist or doctor when I feel like stopping my medication can help keep me on track."

1. _____

_____

2. _____

_____

Thinking about Your Co-occurring Disorders

➤ Describe your thoughts and feelings about having mental health issues and problems with addiction and criminal behavior.

_____

_____

_____

➤ What things do you think played a part in your mental health issues?

_____

_____

_____

➤ Why do you have to work harder at recovery than someone with only one kind of problem?

_____

_____

_____

Your brain uses chemical and electrical energy to send and get messages from the rest of your body.

Your Brain and How It Works

Your brain uses chemical and electrical energy to send and get messages from the rest of your body. The messages might be about pain, temperature, danger, and hunger, for example. When your stomach is empty, your brain gets a signal that your body needs food. A message is sent to your stomach, and you feel hungry. The natural chemicals in your brain that communicate these messages are called neurotransmitters.

Mental health issues can happen when these natural chemicals in your brain get out of balance. Sometimes people are born with them out of balance. For others, the problem happens when they are adults.

When you have a problem in your brain, you might

- feel afraid when there's really nothing to be afraid about
- feel really sad and depressed when your life is actually okay
- hear voices that really aren't there at all— voices no one else can hear

The prescription medicines you take for problems like these are called psychiatric medications. These are *not* like drugs people take to get high, such as alcohol, cocaine, PCP, or meth.

When used the right way, these medicines don't get you high. Instead, they make your brain work normally.

So, you won't feel afraid when there's really nothing to be afraid about. You won't feel really sad when life is actually okay. And the voices that aren't there will become quieter or go away.

This kind of medicine will *not* take away normal painful feelings or get you high. It will only correct any problems in your brain that get in the way of your experiencing a normal life.

Your Body and Brain on Alcohol or Other Drugs

What happens to your body when you are addicted? While the process is complicated, the basic ideas are simple to understand. When you put chemicals in your body that affect your brain, those drugs affect your thinking too. When you are drinking or using, you don't think clearly. As a result, you make unhealthy and poor decisions.

The Pleasure Pathway

Your breathing and heartbeat are controlled by certain areas of the brain. Other parts of the brain respond to pain or pleasure. Here's how it works:

1. Most of your good feelings come from an area in the brain known as the "pleasure pathway." When something good happens to you, your brain makes chemicals that make you feel happy.

2. The "pleasure pathway" is also where drugs like alcohol and cocaine affect the brain. They give you an extra burst of pleasurable feelings.

3. These feelings do not last.

4. The natural level of your brain's own chemicals for making you feel happy goes down when these mood-changing chemicals leave your body.

5. You then feel uncomfortable, sad, depressed, and/or nervous.

6. The more drugs you've been using, the worse you feel when you try to quit. Your body and brain have become used to having the drugs, and they don't like it when they're gone.

7. You don't like these feelings either, so you try to get and take more drugs to get high so you feel better again.

As an addict, you need alcohol or other drugs just to feel okay. Your brain and body are now "addicted" to these drugs. Soon, getting drugs to feel okay becomes the most important thing in your life. That's all you want to do.

The Addicted Brain

The brains of addicted people are different from the brains of nonaddicted people. Drugs like alcohol, cocaine, meth, and marijuana affect addicted people differently. "Normal" people do not experience the intense "high" that addicts love so much.

At some point in an addict's drinking/using history, a change takes place in the brain. This change makes the addict want to use drugs again and again despite negative results.

Once the change happens in your brain to make you an addict, you can't ever go back to "normal." When you start *any* drug use again, no matter how many years have passed since you stopped, the cycle begins again. This is why we know that addiction is a disease. Once the chemistry of addiction is in your brain, it can never be cured. It can only be stopped by not using the drug—and by having a good recovery program.

One of the main causes of relapse:
After you haven't used for a while, you feel healthy. You feel good. You think you're cured. You think you can handle drugs again. But you can't.

Relapse = Incarceration or Death

When you try to stop using drugs, at first you just won't feel quite right. This is "withdrawal." Your body got adjusted to the drugs you were using. While your brain and body heal, you won't feel quite right for a while. It will take some time for your brain to learn to make its own "good feeling" chemicals again *without* drugs. To help your brain get better faster, get enough exercise and sleep, and share your feelings with others.

**Recovery isn't about how not
to use drugs. It's about learning
how to live comfortably
*without having to turn to them.***

Alcohol/Other Drug Use and Your Mental Health Issues

Using alcohol or other drugs is a major risk factor for relapsing into your mental health issues. Alcohol or other drug use affects your mental health. Co-occurring disorders create special problems for treatment and recovery.

Do you remember what Carmen and Terrell said about how using affected them?

In my early twenties, I started hearing voices telling me to hurt my parents. . . . I didn't like the way I felt on the medication they gave me [at the hospital], but maybe that had something to do with the pot I was smoking again. I decided to go off of my meds, and then the voices came back.

— Carmen

I'm in a drug treatment program, but they also have me on a drug because I have what is called "bipolar disorder" and I need the medication to stay level. When I was out on the street, I was into just about everything—dealing drugs, petty theft, and so on. . . . I was drinking and doing a little coke here and there. . . . I began to notice a change. I was feeling "high" even without the cocaine, and that scared me. So I drank more to help me feel normal. Then I felt real low for days at a time. I even would think about killing myself.

— Terrell

Alcohol/Other Drugs

Using alcohol or other drugs can affect your mental health issues by

- triggering the symptoms of your illness, such as manic or depressive episodes

- increasing the stress in your life

- negatively affecting your relationships

- causing you to stay away from your sponsor or hang out with other people who use

- causing you to lose sight of your goals by just "getting high and getting by"

- affecting your brain and body so that medications won't work very well anymore

- increasing the chances that you won't take your medications, skip sessions with a therapist or counselor, or drop out of treatment completely

Mental Health Issues and Relapse Risk

In the same way, mental health issues increase your risk of relapse to using alcohol or other drugs.

Terrell thought drugs would help his mental health issues, but he was wrong.

I was drinking and doing a little coke. . . . I thought I was on top of the world. Then slowly, I began to notice a change. I was feeling "high" even without the cocaine, and that scared me. So I drank more to help me feel normal. Then I felt real low for days at a time. . . . My personal life was a mess. One day, I just couldn't keep it together and decided to knock off a liquor store— and that's how I got here.

Using alcohol or other drugs can affect your mental health issues by negatively affecting your relationships.

Because of your mental health issues, you may

- use alcohol or other drugs to help with or take away the symptoms of your mental health issues

- deny you have an addiction, act without thinking, or think the harmful effects of substances won't bother you

- feel tempted to turn to alcohol and other drugs even after being sober for a long time because of the symptoms connected with your mental illness

- stay away from your friends and not make good use of helping resources that are available to you

EXERCISE **7** EXERCISE

Unhealthy Choices Made While Drinking or Using

➤ Think of some unhealthy choices you made while using drugs (such as getting drunk and smashing a car window, robbing a store, or spending your food money on drugs). List four examples of those choices.

1. _____

2. _____

3. _____

4. _____

Effects of Mental Health Issues on
Your Use of Alcohol or Other Drugs

➤ In what ways have your mental health issues affected your use of alcohol or other drugs?

EXAMPLE: *"When I had a mood swing from mania to depression, I'd usually call my dealer and buy cocaine. I knew this would pick me up."*

List two examples from your own life.

1. _____

_____

_____

_____

_____

2. _____

_____

_____

_____

_____

Effects of Using Alcohol or Other Drugs on Your Mental Health Issues

➤ In what ways has using alcohol or other drugs affected your mental health?

EXAMPLES: *"When I got high on drugs, I just blew off my appointment with my therapist."*

"When I'm high, I stop taking my medication, and that means my symptoms will return."

List two examples from your own life.

1. _____

_____

_____

_____

_____

2. _____

_____

_____

_____

_____

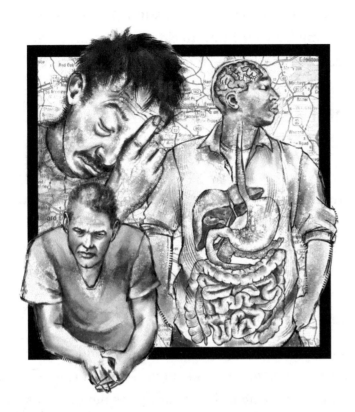

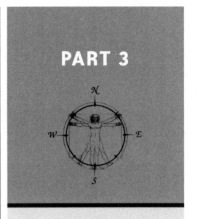

PART 3

Dealing with It: Meds and Treatment

You are probably having problems remembering things, making decisions, or even just thinking. These problems can be signs of drug abuse and addiction *or* they can be signs of a mental health problem. They can *also* be the result of your brain trying to recover from years of substance use.

Heavy use of alcohol and other drugs for a long time can mess up the balance in your brain too. Sometimes it just takes time for your brain to clear out the problems caused by drug use and to return to a more normal state.

Mental Health Issues: Medications Alone Won't Do the Trick

There are different ways you can get help with your mental health issues. You might try counseling, learning new ways to relax, getting treatment for alcoholism and drug addiction, going to support groups, and taking your meds. Some people need to take meds for their mental health issues. Other people do not. That's because counseling and group support help enough for them to get better.

Your doctor or counselor may have told you that you need to take meds for your mental health issues. If that's the case, take time to learn how your medications work, how they can help you, and how to take them exactly like your doctor has told you to.

If you are taking meds, know that they alone *will not* fix the problems in your life. Certainly they can help a lot, but they are not an instant or "magic" solution. But taking meds *can* help you with your mental health issues so you can have a better, happier life.

If you are taking meds, know that they alone *will not* fix the problems in your life.

Before Taking Medications in Recovery

Talking with your mental health provider is the first step to finding what (if any) medications will work for you. Here are the types of questions you can expect the doctor to ask you when you first meet:

- Are you taking any over-the-counter or herbal medicines?
- Do you have any medical problems?
- Have you *ever* had an allergic reaction to medications?
- How did psychiatric medicines you've taken in the past work for you?
- Do you see or hear things that are not there?
- Do you have thoughts of hurting yourself or someone else?
- Do you have a history of alcohol or other drug abuse?
- Have you ever taken doctor-prescribed medications *and* abused other drugs or alcohol at the same time?
- How old are you?
- Do any other members of your family have mental health issues? If so, what medications do they take and are the meds working for them?

Benefits of Taking Your Medications

Doctors carefully prescribe medications for symptoms of mental health issues. Not every medication helps every problem. Here's a list of some of the general ways that taking the *correct type and dose* of prescription medications can help. Taking these medicines

- helps eliminate or reduce voices and visions.
- reduces the false or strange beliefs and ideas that aren't shared by others.

- decreases tension and nervousness: makes you more calm and more relaxed.

- helps you think clearly and concentrate better. Thoughts that are hostile, strange, or aggressive don't happen as often.

- may reduce fears and confusion.

- helps you talk better so others can understand what you are trying to say.

- helps you feel happier and healthier.

- helps you act more normal.

- helps to prevent or delay relapses and the need for being in the hospital again.

About Side Effects—Two Kinds

You may experience side effects from the medicines you're taking. There are two kinds: common and serious.

Common side effects are usually mild. They usually start soon after you start taking the medicine. An example might be a dry mouth or headache. These side effects might get better and even totally go away within two weeks after starting your medicine.

Serious side effects are much rarer. Examples might include dizziness when standing, high blood pressure, severe headaches, rapid weight gain, and blurry vision.

If you are worried about the side effects you are having from a medication, talk to a doctor or other health care provider.

When a doctor gives you a new prescription, ask what side effects that drug can have.

Do's and Don'ts of Taking Medications

There are some common mistakes that people with an addiction often make when they are given medicines for mental health issues, especially for the first time. Here are some good ideas about how to take your medicines.

Do take your medications exactly the way your doctor told you—the exact amount at the right time of day.	**Don't** take your medications just when you feel symptoms.
Do keep taking your medications unless your doctor tells you to stop.	**Don't** stop or change your medications because you feel better or feel they aren't working after a few days or weeks.
Do tell you doctor about all side effects and call right away if you have serious side effects.	**Don't** forget to tell your doctor if you start taking a new prescription medicine or over-the-counter medicine.
Do take your medications at the same time every day. Make the time a habit.	**Don't** share your medications with other people or take their prescriptions.
Do keep going to counseling after you are given medications. Be honest with your doctor about what is happening, even if you relapse. It's *very* important that you keep taking your meds (unless your doctor tells you to stop).	**Don't** use mood-changing drugs (marijuana, meth, alcohol, coke, and so on) when taking your medications.
Do carry a list with you of the medicines you are taking.	**Don't** skip a few days or forget to take your medications. If you do, *don't* take extra doses without talking to a doctor.

Sometimes people will say that recovery from addiction means you have to stop using all drugs—including medicines prescribed by your doctor for mental health issues. That's not true. Alcoholics Anonymous (AA) strongly believes that some people get a lot of help from medications prescribed for psychiatric or medical illnesses.

Effects of Alcohol and Other Drugs on Your Medications

The medicines your doctor prescribed for you have a very special effect on your brain. Using alcohol, cocaine, meth, or other drugs while you are taking your medicines can completely wreck the good effect of your meds and old symptoms will return. What's worse, it's dangerous. For example, using meth or cocaine can actually kill you if you are taking certain antidepressants.

You May Be Tempted, or Pressured, to Stop Taking Your Medications

Some people may not really understand why you're taking medicines for mental health issues. In fact, they may try to talk you out of it. You might even believe some of the things they tell you. Here are some things you'll most likely hear:

1. Aren't these medications addictive, and aren't you just trading one problem for another?

2. You're weak if you use psychiatric medications. You should be able to handle things on your own.

3. You don't need to take your medications every day, just when you feel bad.

4. If you feel worse, hey, just take more pills.

5. It's okay to take other people's medications if you have the same type of problem.

The medicines your doctor prescribed for you have a very special effect on your brain.

6. The medications the doctor gives you should take away all your pain and troubles. So, if they don't do that, forget about them.

7. Watch out. Your medications will change your personality.

8. Don't you have any say in what medications you're told to take? Are you going to let some doctor just tell you what to do?

9. The side effects of medications can make you feel even worse. Maybe you'd be better off not taking the medicines because the side effects will be worse than your problem.

EXERCISE **10** EXERCISE

Taking Your Medications

➤ Look at the list on pages 36–37. Which ones can you most relate to? Pick three that could affect how *you* take your medications. Then, in the space below, write the number of the ones you chose—and how you would deal with these issues.

\# _____ How I would deal with this issue:

_____

_____

_____

_____

_____ How I would deal with this issue:

_____

_____

_____

_____ How I would deal with this issue:

_____

_____

_____

EXERCISE **11** EXERCISE

Looking at Your Symptoms

➤ List two symptoms of your mental health issues that you find most disturbing.

EXAMPLE: *"Sometimes I can't get out of bed, so I miss work."*

1. _____

_____

2. _____

_____

EXERCISE 12 EXERCISE

Positive Effects of Medications

➤ List two positive effects of medications on your symptoms and quality of life.

EXAMPLE: *"When I take my meds like I'm supposed to, life seems so much easier."*

1. _____

   _____

2. _____

   _____

Other Excuses for Not Taking Your Medications

Again, taking your medications as directed is very important for your recovery. Unless you are careful, you'll start making up excuses for not taking them. You might, for example, say to yourself:

- "The side effects from my meds are really bugging me. I'm just going to stop for a few days until they go away. Giving myself a little break will be okay. I deserve it, actually."

- "Hey, now that my symptoms are gone, my illness is cured and I don't need meds anymore. Besides, they're a hassle."

- "I really miss the energy I had, how creative I was, and how much I could do before. I don't have that if I take my medications."

- "My buddies say it's okay to stop."

Using Counseling, Medications, and a Treatment/Recovery Program Together Is the Best Way to Get Better

Remember, medications are only part of recovery. Staying sober, going to group, paying attention to your recovery program, getting exercise, and being in good relationships are all important too. We know that addicts who get *both* medication and treatment have the best chance to succeed in making a better life.

Accept Your Mental Health Issues

Admitting that you have co-occurring disorders is a big step in getting better. If you aren't ready to accept that, you probably won't work at your recovery, take your meds, or go to therapy. You didn't choose to have the hand you have been dealt, though some decisions you've made (drinking and using) may have made your problems worse. It doesn't matter how it happened. No matter what, it *is* your responsibility to work hard to manage your co-occurring disorders.

Change Your Thinking

Your feelings and behavior are affected by your thoughts and beliefs about yourself and the world. One way to change negative thinking is to find and challenge thoughts that make your symptoms or problems worse. When you have negative thoughts such as "I'm a failure," "Life won't get any better," or "I can't live without booze or other drugs," you need to challenge them.

Change Your Behaviors

There is no quick fix for your problems—you will have to work hard at recovery. You will need to change some behaviors that are tied to your personality. This is a step that comes after you've been sober and well for a while.

Here are some examples of changes that other people made:

Darnell worked hard at being a more responsible husband and father, instead of always putting himself first. He also quit blaming others or society for his problems—he realized that it was up to him to take control of his life.

Charlene quit doing everything that others wanted her to do. She began to think about herself for a change, rather than always taking care of others. Charlene learned to say no.

EXERCISE **13** EXERCISE

Making Change Happen

➤ Think about a behavior in your life that you would like to change.

_____

_____

➤ List two steps you can take to make this change happen.

1. _____

_____

2. _____

_____

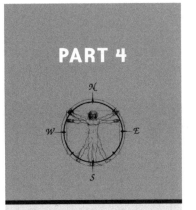

Relapse

With addiction, relapse is the process of going back to alcohol or other drug use. In the case of mental health issues, relapse happens when your symptoms return. Or it can happen when you start thinking about not taking your medications or actually stop taking them.

For people with mental health issues, relapse happens when they

- start using alcohol or other drugs *instead* of taking their medications

- stop taking their medications altogether or regularly

- start taking their medications *along with* alcohol or other drugs (which means their meds won't work anymore)

Relapse can mean that the symptoms of your mental health issues come back after a period of getting better. You can be in a state of relapse even *before* you start using again or stop taking your meds. The effects of a relapse depend on how bad it is and whether you do something quickly to get help.

Causes of Relapse

Many things can lead to relapse. Returning mental health problems can make you feel like using alcohol or other drugs again. And using alcohol or other drugs can trigger symptoms of your mental health issues.

Relapse is usually caused by a combination of things working together. Here are some of the most common causes of relapse for people with co-occurring disorders:

- emotional stress—feeling very upset, angry, depressed, alone or isolated, empty, useless, or overwhelmed

- lifestyle choices—having no routines or goals in your life, or having a major life change, such as being sick or the death of a family member or loss of a job

- bad relationships—having serious trouble with someone, feeling unloved or not connected to others, or feeling stuck in bad relationships that cause a lot of pain

- the people you hang out with—spending time with people who abuse alcohol or other drugs, or people who try to get you to stop treatment

- ignoring early relapse warning signs—not doing anything when your symptoms return or get worse

- missing meetings—not going to AA, NA, or other sober support groups

- messing with your meds—stopping your meds or not taking them the way you are supposed to

- not following your treatment plan—missing appointments with your doctor, therapist, or counselor

- telling yourself that you're cured—deciding that since you haven't had bad symptoms for a while, you don't need your meds anymore

- not being responsible—wanting others to solve your problems or not listening to the advice of your sponsor

Relapse Prevention

Making a good relapse prevention plan is something you need to do. This is the plan that lays out the steps you need to take to avoid relapse. You need help to do this. You need to have people in your life who can help you, even when you don't think you need help.

Carmen's story shows that it is possible to manage ongoing symptoms and stay in recovery.

> *The voices are still with me. They are not too bad as long as I take my medication and don't smoke weed. I've been sober now for two years, and they say that if I stay sober and keep managing my symptoms, I will probably be released.*

Relapse Warning Signs

Relapse doesn't just happen. There are *always* warning signs that you're getting close to a relapse. People who have relapsed know that there were many clues long before it happened. Your thinking will "slip" or "lapse" before an actual relapse. Examples might be staying away from your AA or NA meeting and hanging out with people you used to drink or use with.

These slips or lapses are *relapse warning signs*. They show up in your thinking, your moods, behavior, attitudes, feelings, health habits, and daily routines. Recognize your lapses—*before* you've actually *done* something that violates your parole, that hurts someone, that's illegal. You have to act immediately when you notice these signs!

SUDs—Seemingly Unimportant Decisions

Often, an actual relapse act can't be carried out right away. That's because the time isn't right. Instead, you relapse "in your mind" by making secret plans or having fantasies. You then rationalize them away or deny having done this, or both. This denial and rationalizing come together to create a chain of events leading to a relapse.

People who are headed for a relapse make a number of small decisions in that direction over time. The term "SUDs" (seemingly unimportant decisions) describes these decisions. Each decision brings them a little bit closer to relapse. Recovering alcoholics who buy a twelve-pack of beer to take home "just in case friends drop by" are setting themselves up for relapse. In the same way, people with mental health issues who say "I don't really need my meds today" or "I'll be okay if I miss my doctor's appointment today" are also making a SUD that is setting them up for relapse.

There are always warning signs that you're getting close to a relapse.

When you "set up" a relapse like this, it gives you an excuse to not be responsible for the relapse. By putting yourself in high-risk situations, it becomes "impossible" to resist relapse. The reality is that *you* put yourself in this position. You are *always* the one who is responsible for your behavior.

You need to pay attention to changes that are happening and do something about them *before* you relapse.

If you notice your relapse warning signs early on, you can stop your behavior before relapse starts—or before things get really bad.

Warning: Relapse Ahead

The process of relapse includes changes in thoughts and attitudes, feelings and moods, and behaviors. By knowing *your* warning signs, you can make a plan to deal with them. In turn, your recovery will go better.

EXERCISE **14** EXERCISE

Exercise 14 is from *Preventing Relapse* by Dennis Daley (Center City, MN: Hazelden, 2003). It has been adapted for use here.

Changing Behavior

➤ Place an **X** next to any of the following statements that you can relate to now or in the past:

____ I've missed a bunch of sessions with my therapist.

____ I quit going to treatment.

____ I quit taking my meds or didn't take them like I was supposed to.

____ I cut down or stopped going to AA or NA.

_____ I don't like to call my sponsor anymore.

_____ I don't like to work anymore.

_____ I try to pick fights with others.

_____ People sometimes say I act very strange or bizarre.

_____ I just want to be by myself.

_____ I don't like doing anything that doesn't involve doing drugs or drinking alcohol.

Review the statements you chose. Choose two that you can relate to most right now. Then complete this exercise.

➤ **First relapse warning sign**
Write one of the statements here.

_____

_____

Relapse prevention plan—coping ideas I can use to manage this trigger:

1. _____

_____

2. _____

_____

3. _____

_____

4. _____

_____

➤ **Second relapse warning sign**
Write another statement here.

_____

_____

Relapse prevention plan—coping ideas I can use to manage this trigger:

1. _____

_____

2. _____

_____

3. _____

_____

4. _____

_____

Daily Symptom and Problem Checklist

My usual rating for my symptoms of anxiety and depression was three. But lately, both went up to six. This made me see that my symptoms were getting worse. I called my counselor, and she and I worked together on ways I could lower my feelings of anxiety and depression.

— Carmen

My usual rating for suicidal thoughts was one or two. In the last week or so, it went up to seven. I followed my plan to tell my counselor and group about any ratings that went up. We worked together, and I was able to get over my thoughts of hurting myself and didn't have to go back to the hospital.

— Terrell

Start paying close attention to your thoughts, feelings, behaviors, mental health issues, and urges to use alcohol or other drugs. Doing this will help you spot your relapse warning signs early. Keeping a daily checklist can help you keep on top of your recovery and prevent relapse.

Like Carmen and Terrell, the sooner you can catch changes in your symptoms or problems, the quicker you can take action and get help. If some of your symptoms are always there, a relapse would mean that a symptom gets worse. Carmen, for example, still hears voices (hallucinations) even though she takes her medication and sees a counselor. She's learned to live with the voices, but she lets her doctor and counselor know if the voices become stronger and get in the way of her day-to-day living.

Daily Rating of Symptom or Problem Severity

Exercise 15 is from *Preventing Relapse* by Dennis Daley (Center City, MN: Hazelden, 2003). It has been adapted for use here.

➤ The following chart lists the relapse triggers included in exercise 14. You can also write in additional triggers you have. Rate how severe each of the symptoms on the chart is for you (see rating scale below). Put your rating next to the symptom or problem *each day* of the week, using a number from 1 to 10 (10 is the most severe).

EXAMPLE:

Rating Scale

0	3	5	7	10
None at all	Mild	Moderate	Strong	Extreme

Symptom or Problem	M	T	W	Th	F	Sa	Su
Desire to drink alcohol.	2	3	3	1	2	7	4

Rating Scale

0	3	5	7	10
None at all	Mild	Moderate	Strong	Extreme

Symptom or Problem	M	T	W	Th	F	Sa	Su
I've missed a bunch of sessions with my therapist.							
I quit going to treatment.							
I quit taking my meds or didn't take them the way I was supposed to.							
I cut down or stopped going to AA or NA.							
I don't like to call my sponsor anymore.							
I don't like to work anymore.							
I try to pick fights with others.							
People sometimes say I act very strange or bizarre.							
I just want to be by myself.							
I don't like doing anything that doesn't involve doing drugs or drinking alcohol.							

Dealing with Feelings

It's important to learn how to recognize and manage *both* positive and negative feelings. Knowing how to deal with your feelings can improve your mental health and relationships with others. It can also lower your chances of using again.

Here are some common feelings that are connected with relapse:

- frustrated
- resentful
- worried
- bored
- empty
- feeling great
- fearful
- panicked
- guilty
- lonely
- sorry for yourself

It's important to learn how to recognize and manage both positive and negative feelings.

You can expect to have many different feelings during recovery. Having feelings isn't a problem. What matters is how you *deal with* the feelings. For example, everyone feels lonely, bored, or worried sometimes. But if you start to feel very depressed when you have these feelings, or if you have strong urges to drink or use, then it's important to have a plan in place to deal with this. For example, you might call your sponsor or a friend before you have that strong urge to drink or use.

Having positive feelings can be dangerous too. For example, feeling great might tempt you to stop seeing your counselor or to stop taking your meds. This can lead to relapse.

Feelings have to come out eventually. Some people let out their feelings in a positive way. Others let their feelings build up inside. When those feelings finally come out, they can be out of control. As a result, sometimes they say or do things that they later regret.

Letting out positive feelings such as appreciation and being happy is important too. Doing this will make you feel better and help you stay away from using and criminal activity.

EXERCISE **16** EXERCISE

Looking at Feelings

This exercise will help you identify feelings you want to work on and to make a plan to do that.

➤ List five feelings that can lead to relapse for you, for example, guilty, hopeless, lonely, overwhelmed, happy, or excited. You can select feelings listed on page 53 or write down your own.

1. _____

2. _____

3. _____

4. _____

5. _____

➤ Once you've listed five feelings, fill in the blanks with the feelings and then complete the following sentences:

1. I feel _____ when

_____

_____

2. I feel _____ when

_____

_____

3. I feel _____ when

_____

_____

4. I feel _____ when

_____

_____

5. I feel _____ when

_____

_____

In the past, feelings controlled your attitudes and actions. Now you can have feelings *without* allowing them to control you. Here's how to do it: instead of reacting to feelings in a negative way, make a plan to do something positive.

➤ Show how you will act in a positive way by completing the following sentences using the feelings you identified on the previous pages.

EXAMPLE: *"When I feel lonely, I will call a friend."*

1. When I feel _____ I will

_____

_____

2. When I feel _____ I will

_____

_____

3. When I feel _____ I will

_____

_____

4. When I feel _____ I will

_____

_____

5. When I feel _____ I will

_____

_____

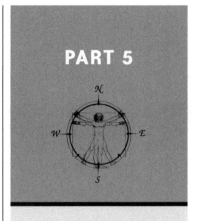

Building a Support System

No one can recover alone. You will need help to recover from your addiction and psychiatric illness—and that help is available, even behind bars. Get that help now.

Help can come from

- Alcoholics Anonymous (AA)

- Narcotics Anonymous (NA)

- Dual Disorders Anonymous (DDA)

- prison ministries, groups, and meetings

You can also find help through other abstinence-based groups such as

- Men for Sobriety

- Women for Sobriety

- Emotions Anonymous

- Secular Organizations for Sobriety/
  Save Our Selves (SOS)

- Walking the Red Road

A support system is important in your recovery. Your support system should include people such as your doctor, therapist, sober family members, and others who support your new sober lifestyle. You can use them

- for emotional support

- to talk about a problem

- to talk about thoughts of dropping out of treatment

- to talk about a strong desire to use alcohol or other drugs

- to find positive sober activities

- to have them point out relapse warning signs before you see them

Talk regularly with these people. Remember, it's *your job* to cope with warning signs if someone points them out. People who have a good support system have a better chance of staying in recovery.

Your Support System

➤ List the names and phone numbers of four people you can rely on for support and help in recovering from your illnesses.

Person #1 and phone number:

_____

Person #2 and phone number:

_____

Person #3 and phone number:

_____

Person #4 and phone number:

_____

➤ List the four most important things you need to ask them to help you with.

1. _____

2. _____

3. _____

4. _____

Progress, Not Perfection

You can be very proud of the efforts you've made so far in your recovery from drinking and using, and with your mental health issues. You'll notice the benefits of sobriety when positive changes start happening in your life.

What to Do When Emergencies Happen

No matter how hard you work at recovery, there is always a chance that you could relapse. This is why you should prepare for emergencies. This way, if you start to relapse, you can catch it early and take action to get back on track quickly. If the symptoms of your mental health issues return or worsen, or if you start using alcohol or other drugs, get help right away.

Talk about emergency situations with people in your support group. They can help you get the help you need if things get bad. Tell the people in your support group how you want them to help. Put your plan in writing as a reminder, because if you get sick again, you might not remember that you ever had such a talk with them.

Planning for an Emergency

➤ List two steps you can take if you start using alcohol or
other drugs:

1. _____

   _____

2. _____

   _____

➤ List two steps you can take if you have a mental health
emergency:

1. _____

   _____

2. _____

   _____

The best way to head off emergencies is to ask for help
immediately. Once things settle down again, you can try to
figure out what caused the emergency.

You Can Do This

You may think of recovery as a difficult and endless task. It's time to change your thinking. It's time to think in a new way about these changes. If you think of recovery as hard, like going on a diet, it just won't work.

Look at it as a new adventure, because that is exactly what it is. Accept the support others are giving you. Your new life will offer you so much that you won't want to give it up.

And your life *will* change. By showing up, staying sober, and working on your recovery program, you'll eventually see the benefits. After a while, staying in balance won't seem like something you *have* to do, but something you *want* to do. You will begin to truly like the new person you've become. By doing this work, your life will look brighter. This is not a dream or a trick or a con. You *can* reach a point where you *want* to be in recovery—a point where your passion for recovery is as strong as your passion for drinking and using and crime once was.

This workbook has provided help and given you a start on the road to recovery. You *can* recover. You *can* create better relationships and live a richer, more fulfilling life. Reach out to others for strength, support, and encouragement. Everything that you *need* will be given to you.

Start thinking in a new way

Thinking Report

1. **Event** _____
   _____
   _____
   _____
   _____

2. **Thoughts** _____
   _____
   _____
   _____
   _____

3. **Feelings** _____
   _____
   _____
   _____
   _____

4. **Behavior** _____
   _____
   _____
   _____
   _____

NOTES

NOTES